Violet Rose

and
THE VERY SNOWY WINTER

Contents

Welcome to Sunnyville!

Welcome to Sunnyville, the friendly hometown of Violet Rose! Winter has arrived, bringing with it snow and ice. But today the sun is shining, so Violet and her neighbours are out having fun. Have a look around and see what everyone is up to!

I'm Arthur. I love to play in the snow!

Hello, I'm Lily!

I'm Twinkles!

Hi, I'm Violet! Welcome to chilly Sunnyville!

I'm Sprinkles!

Violet's best friend, Betsy, lives here. The two pals often spend their evenings working on craft and chatting!

Come for a spin on my ice rink!

Florence's Flowers

I'm Betsy! Nice to meet you!

Welcome to our town!

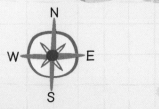

N W E S

Build your own Sunnyville

You can build your very own winter Sunnyville using the press-out card pieces on the opposite page. Just follow the steps below!

You will need glue for this activity.

Step 1

Gently remove the whole page of press-out pieces by tearing the long perforated line down the middle of the book. Then carefully press out each piece, one by one.

Tear here

Step 2

Fold along the scored lines. Try to make your folds as clean and as crisp as you can!

Fold

Step 3

Apply glue to all the areas marked with pink cross-hatching and then press them to the areas with blue cross-hatching. Match up the areas according to their numbers – so the area marked 1 should be stuck to the other area marked 1, 2 with 2, and so on.

Step 4

You can download and print out more Sunnyville buildings at www.worldofvioletrose.com! For best results, use A4 card or stiff paper in your printer.

You might need a grown-up to help you!

Build your own Sunnyville – page 4

Fold one flap forward and one flap back on each character.

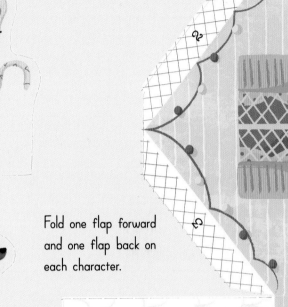

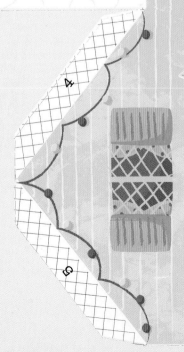

5

2

3

4

1

Build your own Sunnyville
– page 4

Dressing up

After a busy morning doing their chores, Violet, Fred and Mia have decided to go out and have fun in the snow. But first they must dress up warmly. Can you help put on their cold-weather outfits?

Use the stickers on page 11 to complete the scene!

Snowy fun

It seems that the whole of Sunnyville has had the same idea! Everyone has come up the mountain to ski, sledge and play in the snow. But, oh dear, it looks like Mia's gone too fast and had an accident. She'll have to go to the hospital!

Use the stickers on page 11 to complete the scene!

Dressing up – page 9

Snowy fun – page 10

Mountain maze

The ambulance team has picked Mia up and they are heading back down the mountainside with their siren blaring. Can you help them find the right road to Sunnyville hospital?

At the hospital

Violet and her friends arrive at the hospital just as Mia is brought in by the paramedics. Her leg is very sore so she will need to have an X-ray to see if it's broken. It looks like a few other people have injured themselves in the snow, too!

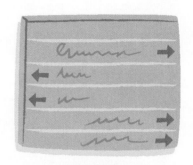

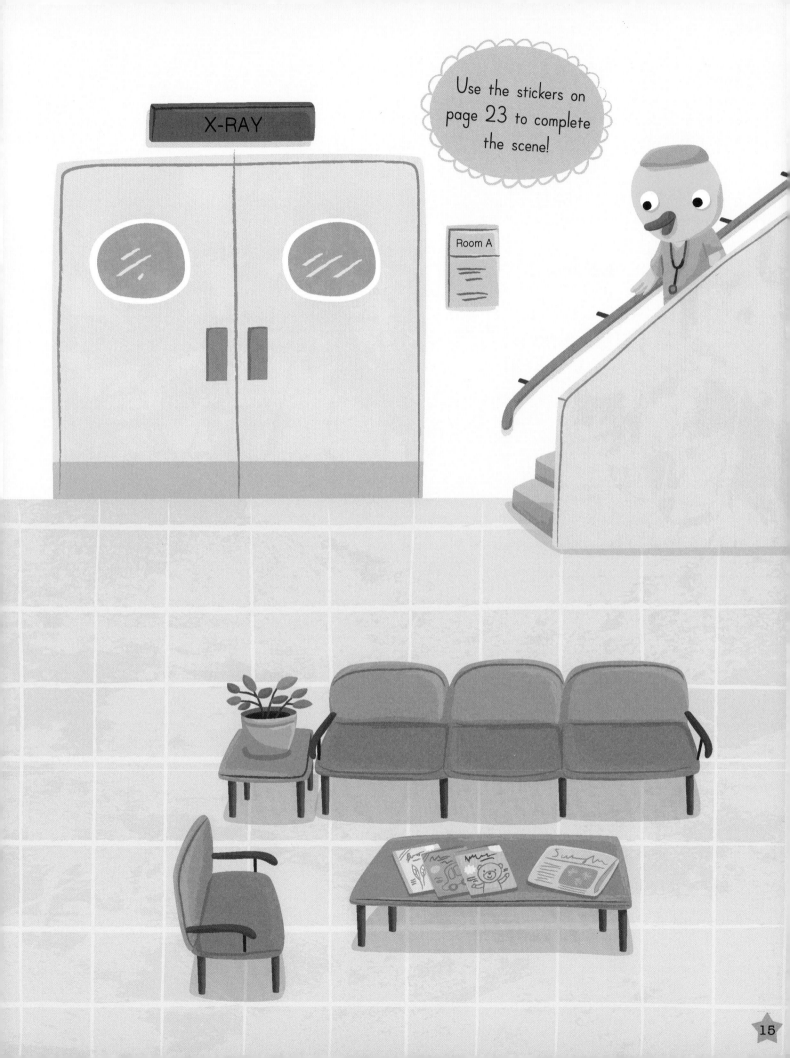

X-RAY

Room A

Use the stickers on page 23 to complete the scene!

Christmas cards

Violet and Betsy are happy to be back at Betsy's house now. Christmas is coming soon so they decide to start sending out their Christmas cards!

Use your thumbnail to make a nice, sharp fold down each card!

Step 1

The first thing to do when sending out Christmas cards is to write a list of the people you want to send cards to. Then you know how many cards you have to write!

Step 2

Gently tear out page 17. Then carefully press out each piece, one by one, and fold each card in half.

Step 3

Write in each card, making sure you say who the card is to and who it's from!

Step 4

Press out the gift-tags and thread them onto some string or ribbon. Keep them for present-wrapping time.

For printable wrapping paper, envelopes and more cards go to www.worldofvioletrose.com

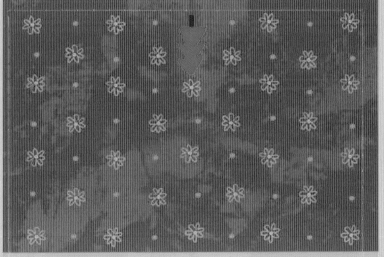

Merry
Christmas!

Season's
Greetings

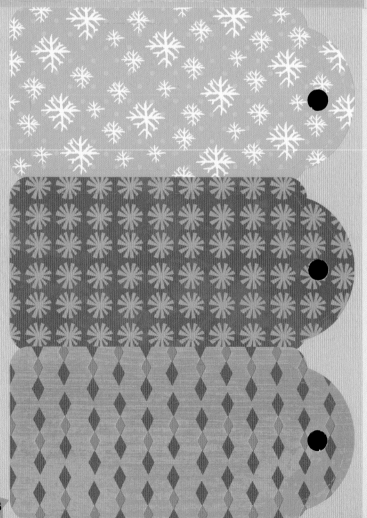

Happy
Holidays!

Woollen stockings

Next day it's snowing, so Violet and Betsy stay indoors by the cosy fire. They get started on knitting Christmas stockings for all their friends!

Can you help them finish the stockings? You'll need felt-tip pens or coloured pencils!

A really great idea

One by one, Violet's friends arrive to take shelter from the cold. Just as they start baking cookies for tea, Pinkerton has a really great idea! He says that they should make decorations and presents for the people at the hospital!

A woodland journey

Meanwhile, just up the road, Sprinkles and Twinkles are in their houses. The twins are worried about their grandparents who live in the woods, so they have decided to take them some food and warm clothes.

Sprinkles and Twinkles love to do everything the same way, but there are some differences between these two pictures – can you spot them?

There are 12 differences to spot!

At the hospital –
page 14

A really great idea – page 20

Gift wrapping

Back at Betsy's house, the friends are very pleased with all the decorations and presents they have made for the people at the hospital. Can you help them finish the pretty wrapping paper?

You'll need felt-tip pens or coloured pencils for this activity.

A gorgeous garland

As a finishing touch, the friends make a beautiful garland as a decoration for the hospital. But just then, Violet receives a phone call from Sprinkles and Twinkles. Oh dear, they are lost in the woods!

You can hang your garland in your bedroom!

Step 1

To make your own garland, carefully tear out page 27, then press out each piece. Using a pencil, gently push out the small holes in each shape. You will need a piece of string or thin ribbon that's at least two metres long.

Step 2

One by one, thread each shape onto the string or ribbon.

For more printable garlands go to www.worldofvioletrose.com

Oh no, Sprinkles and Twinkles need our help!

27

Lost in the woods!

Can you help Violet and her friends guide Sprinkles and Twinkles through the woods and back to Sunnyville?

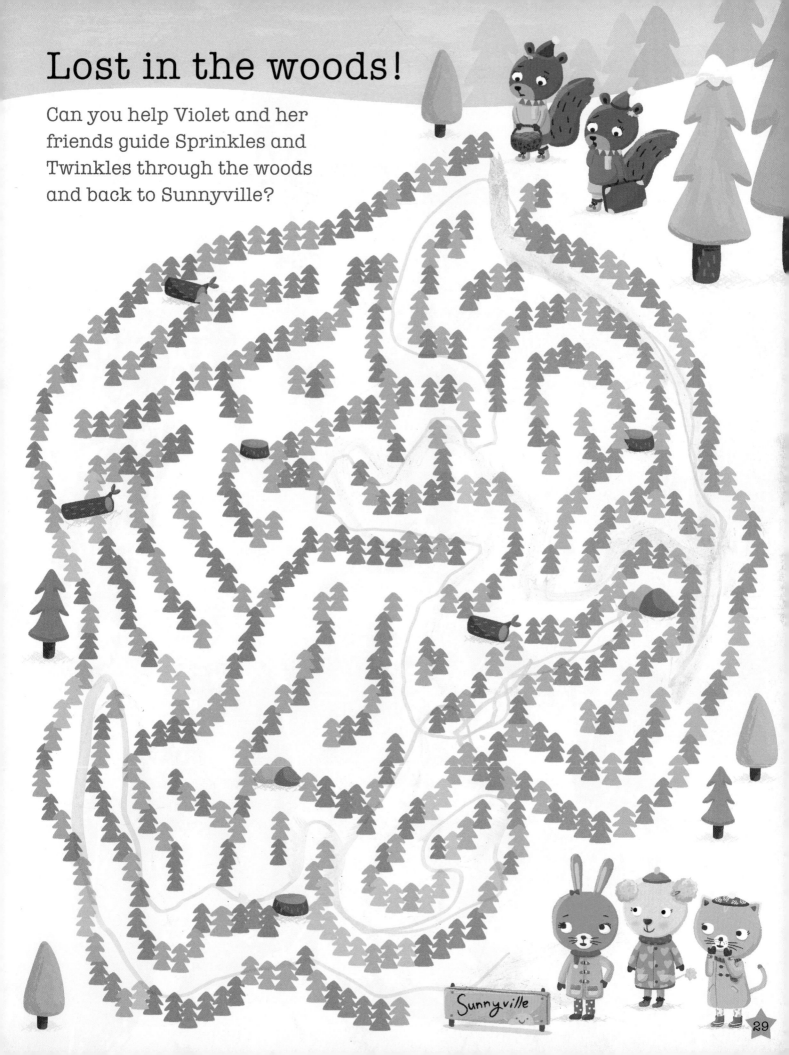

Sunnyville

A surprise for the hospital

Luckily, Sprinkles and Twinkles made it back to
Sunnyville safe and sound. Now they've come with
Violet and their friends to visit Mia in hospital.
They've brought all the Christmas decorations,
and gifts for the doctors, nurses and patients, too!

Use the stickers on
page 33 to decorate
the hospital ward!

What a pretty tree!

The hospital Christmas tree looks a bit plain! Can you help the friends cover it in baubles and decorations so it looks super sparkly?

Use the stickers on page 33 to decorate the tree!

Tear here

33

Presents for everyone

Violet and her friends are giving presents to everyone on the ward. Can you guess who gets which gift? Then follow the line to see if you were right!

A very big shopping list

It's Christmas Eve now, and Violet has come to the market to do her last-minute shopping. Can you help her to find all of the items she needs to cook her Christmas feast?

Shopping List

- 12 x potatoes ☐
- 20 x carrots ☐
- 3 x cabbages ☐
- 1 x jug of cream ☐
- 7 x oranges ☐
- 4 x loaves of bread ☐
- 1 x bag of flour ☐
- 10 x gingerbread men ☐
- 5 x cheeses ☐
- 21 x Brussel sprouts ☐
- 6 x lemons ☐

Snowman competition

On her way home from her shopping trip, Violet bumps into her friends. They are having a snowman-building contest and they want Violet to be the judge! Which snowman should get the prize, do you think?

Use the stickers on page 39 to finish the snowmen!

38

Tear here

A moonlit walk
– page 42

A festive feast with friends – page 49

Christmas concert

Violet has arranged to meet her friends at the Christmas Eve carol concert in the town hall. They have all arrived – but so has everyone else in town! Can you help Violet to find her pals?

A moonlit walk

After the concert, the friends walk back home through Sunnyville, wishing their neighbours a happy Christmas. With the stars twinkling in the bright night sky, it is such a magical night!

Use the stickers on page 39 to complete the scene!

Finishing touches

As Violet cooks the Christmas feast for her friends, Audrey and Fred make some angel decorations and some place cards to put on the dining table.

You will need some pretty thread and a pen for this activity.

Step 1

Gently remove the whole of pages 45 and 47 by tearing the long perforated line down the middle of the book. Then carefully press out each piece, one by one.

Tear here

For printable angels and place cards go to www.worldofvioletrose.com

Step 2

Curl the angel shape around and slot together slits A and B. Tape a loop of string to the back of each head.

Step 3

Press out each place card and fold along the dotted lines. Write your guests' names in the space provided.

Mia

Violet

Tear here

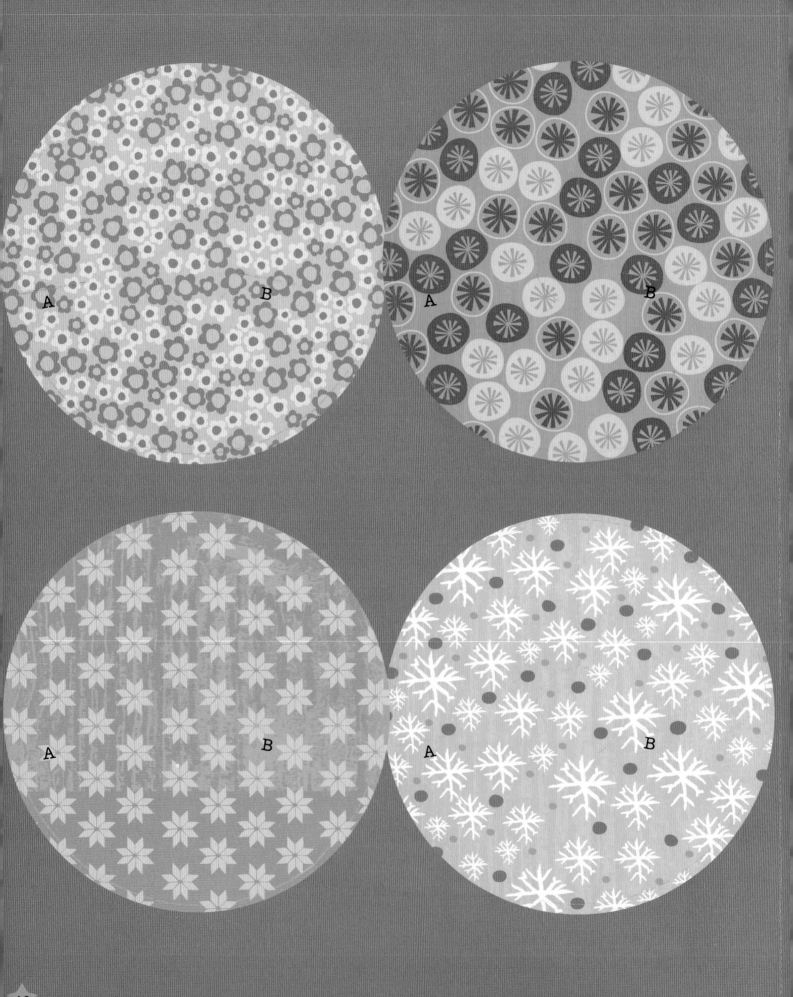

A   B

A   B

A   B

A   B

Tear here

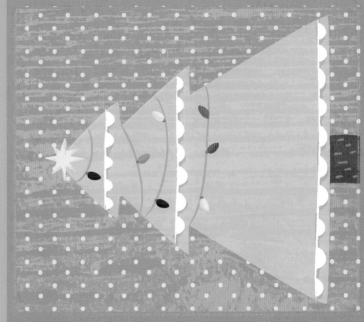

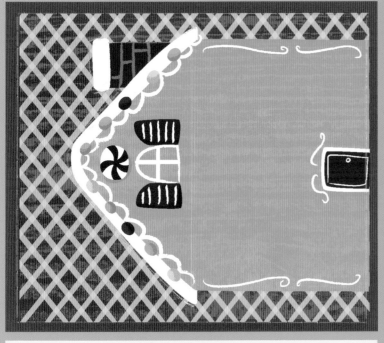

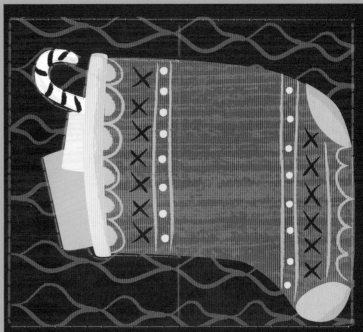

A festive feast with friends

What a merry Christmas gathering! All the friends are so happy to be sharing Christmas with each other.

Use the stickers on page 39 to complete the scene!

A Christmas Day visitor

Christmas Day is here, and look who
has arrived – it's Father Christmas,
and he's brought presents for Violet
and all of her friends! What a wonderful
surprise – Merry Christmas, everybody!

Complete the scene using felt-tip pens or coloured pencils.

51

Violet's diary

It has been a very busy Christmas for Violet! When life is back to normal again, she takes time to remember what has happened and writes it all down in her diary.

Fill in the gaps with a pencil!

Dear Diary,

It certainly has been a Christmas to remember!

It all started when we went out into the snow and .... had an accident. She hurt her .... and had to go to the .... in an ambulance!

After we'd been to the hospital, we decided to make .... for the ward, and .... to give to the patients – and the doctors and nurses as well!

.... and .... went to visit their grandparents but they got lost and had to be ....!

My favourite part of Christmas was.................... I am so happy that I have so many....................friends to share this special holiday with.

Love Violet xxx

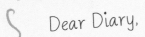